C000001906

American Tundra She
20 Milestone Challenges

American Tundra Shepherd Dog Memorable Moments.
Includes Milestones for Memories, Gifts, Grooming,
Socialization & Training

Volume 2

Todays Doggy

Copyright © 2019

Dedicated To All of You Wonderful Owners and Fans

Introduction

Welcome to the Original Doggy Milestone Series™ where you are encouraged to create those special moments with your dog. We have composed the milestones in a way that challenges you to set the stage before taking your photos.

Use props and make it fun - be creative in setting up your photos. Get family and friends involved - take it out with you - use it in different places and settings - have a play with it and most importantly, have a good time!

You can either hold the desired milestone spread open yourself - or have somebody hold it open as you take the snap.

If you would like to have the selected milestone book spread open and standing independently in your photos, you can use one or two large 'foldback' clips to hold the spread open.

Share your photos with friends, family, and communities - look for feedback and areas of improvements in order to create even better memorable photos.

Good luck and enjoy your photo fun.

I Noticed You Were Sleeping...

So I Helped You Finish The Food

I Look Rather Fetching

...Don't I ?

SORRY...

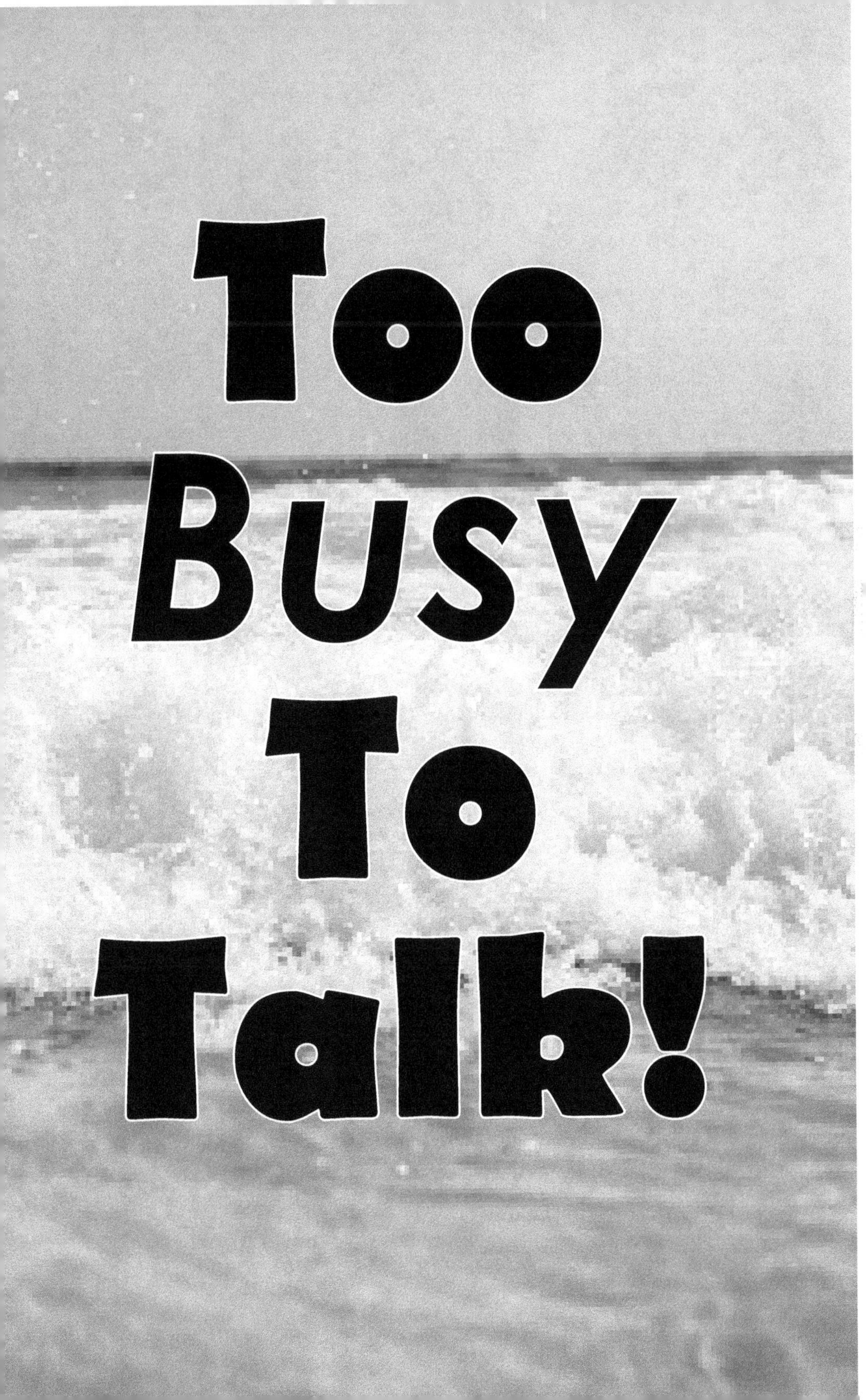
Too
Busy
To
Talk!

...Bad To The Bone

Today...

Was a "RUFF!" Day

I Have No Idea

What I'm Doing

WHEN YOU'RE HOME ALONE

AND
SOMEONE KNOCKS ON THE DOOR...

MIRROR MIRROR ON THE WALL...

Who's The Doggiest Of Them All?

I'm So GREAT

I Even Know How To High 5

Ahh...

The Joys of Being Groomed

You're Home Early!

I'm Not Lazy

I'm Just On Energy Saving Mode

OH LOOK!

Someone Has Made a Mess!

I Wonder Who Did It!?

As You Can See

I'm
Sleeping

Your Secrets Are Safe With Me

I'm Always Listening

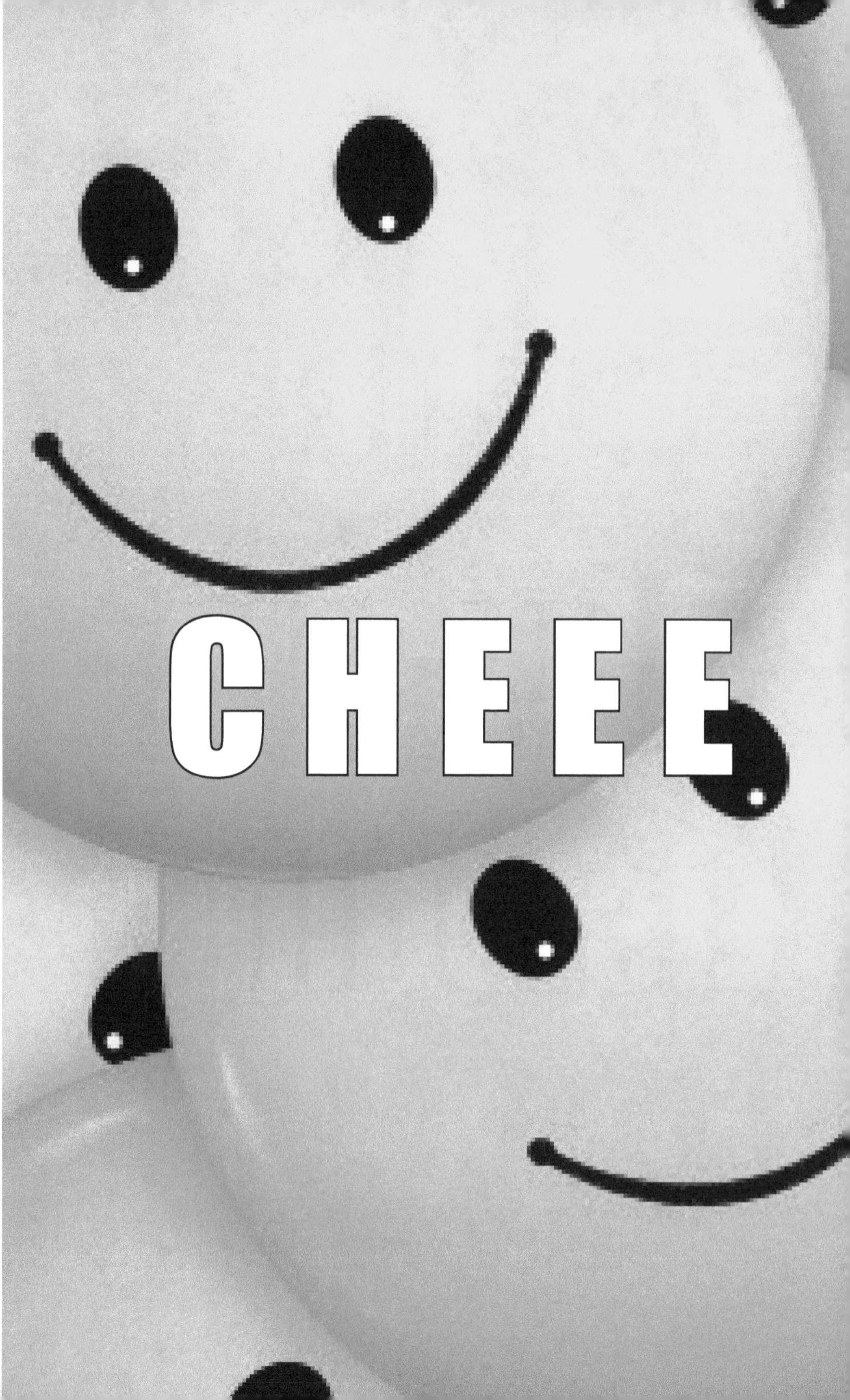
CHEEE

EEEESE

My Dog's Reaction When I Say...

I'm
Ready

For My Bedtime Story

I've Got It All...

Under

Control

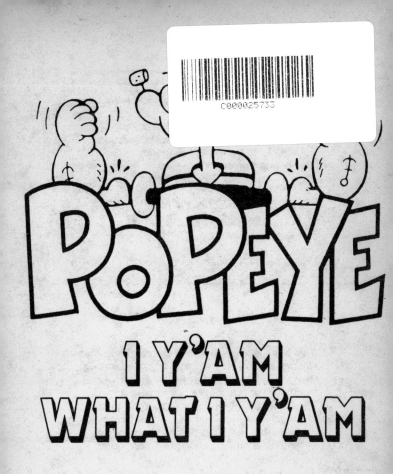

POPEYE

I Y'AM
WHAT I Y'AM

RAVETTE BOOKS

Printed and bound in Great Britain
for Ravette Books Limited,
3 Glenside Estate, Star Road, Partridge Green,
Horsham, West Sussex RH13 8RA
by Cox & Wyman Ltd, Reading

ISBN 1 85304 192 0

™

3-10

MY NEW DIGITAL WATCH TELLS THE DAY, THE MONTH, THE YEAR, THE TEMPERATURE, YOUR HOROSCOPE, HOW MANY DAYS TILL CHRISTMAS, AND IT STORES PHONE NUMBERS AND RECIPES, TOO.

WHAT TIME IS IT?

DON'T GET PICKY, POPEYE.

4-9

6·23

7-15

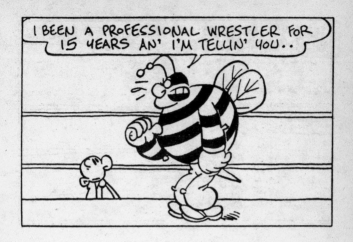

4-19

4-30

5-10

7-19

4-27

5-27

7-31